DannY
The Champion of the World

ISBN: 9781904806158

Imaginative Minds Ltd
215 The Green House
Gibb Street
Digbeth
Birmingham
B9 4AA

IM
IMAGINATIVE
MINDS

Danny The Champion of the World.
First published by Jonathan Cape 1975.
Published by Puffin Books 1977.

First published 1992.
Author Linda Evans
Cover illustration Iqbal Aslam 1992
Production and Design Iqbal Aslam

Contents

Danny The Champion of the World

Notes for the Teacher

A book like "Danny the Champion of the World" can provide starting points for countless activities which will cover all the Attainment Targets for English in the National Curriculum - as well as being a "good read". These worksheets have been designed to accompany the reading of the book, by the whole class or a smaller group within the class, and maximise its potential as stimulus material. They should, in the main, follow teacher- led discussion rather than be totally self-supporting.

The worksheets do not follow a pattern of easy-average-difficult assignments, but include a good variety of activities which make different kinds of demands on the pupil. For example, the first set of worksheets cover the introduction to Danny, his father and their life together. The first is presented in simple terms, asking direct questions which relate to pupils' own experience and opinions. The second sheet requires some research and a measure of creativity, while the third involves pupils in thinking about the use of language for different purposes and using skills of inference.

Teachers who see a need for "differentiated" tasks often lack the necessary resources: these worksheets are an attempt to provide work for children of varying abilities and aptitudes, in an interesting and varied way, which will enhance the reading of the book rather than elicit cries of:

"We haven't gotta WRITE about it have we, Miss?"

DannY
The Champion of the World

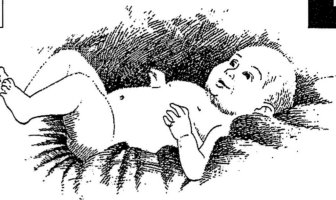

"While I was still a baby, my father washed me and fed me and changed my nappies and did all the millions of other things a mother normally does for her child."

1. Who looked after you when you were a baby?

2. Do you think it is harder for a man to look after a baby? Why?

3. Why was it especially difficult for Danny's father?

4. Make a list of all the things you have to do when you are caring for a baby.

5. Is it easier to look after a baby now than it was twenty or thirty years ago? Why?

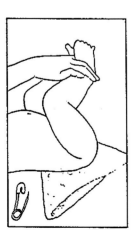
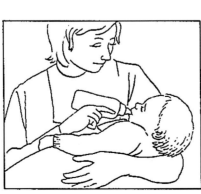
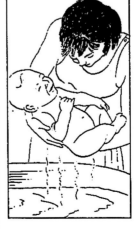
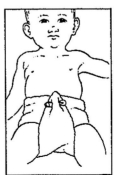

DannY
The Champion of the World

"There was only one room in the caravan..."

Read the last seven paragraphs of Chapter 1 again.

1. How was living in the gypsy caravan different from living in a modern house?

2. Would you like to live in a caravan like Danny's? Why?

3. With a partner, make a list of all the different types of homes you can think of. (Look in the library to find out more.)

4. What would be the perfect home for you? Describe it as well as you can.

"The filling station itself had only two pumps..."

"The square brick building to the right of the office was the workshop..."

"The caravan was our house and our home..."

Imagine that Danny and his father are leaving their home. They put up a FOR SALE sign and place an advertisement in the newspaper.

Write out the advertisement to describe the property as fully as possible, (Look at the property ads in your local newspaper and find out which abbreviations are commonly used - e.g. det., mod., trad., lux. etc.)

Try to convey, in the way you write the ad, how Danny and his father felt about their home.

What type of people might be interested in buying such a home? Write a short play about the prospective buyer visiting Danny and his father.

DannY
The Champion of the World

"My father without the slightest doubt, was the most marvellous and exciting father any boy ever had."

Perhaps most fathers would not come up to Danny's expectations. Lots of young people might think that their dads are dull and boring. They probably have other <u>attributes</u>* though, like kindness, patience and generosity.

1. Describe your own dad, grandad or uncle. Write the description in two parts:-

a) What he looks like, the clothes he wears.

b) What sort of person he is, what he likes and dislikes, and his work and hobbies.

2. Danny thinks that his dad is the best in the world. Which qualities do <u>you</u> think would make the perfect father?

* <u>attributes</u> are good qualities in a person.

3. 'My Dad, Your Dad' is a poem by Kit Wright which paints an amusing picture of two fathers. Read this poem and decide how the two youngsters feel about their dads.

The Big Friendly Giant

What does the BFG look like?

You will find clues on the following pages:-

p.13	paragraph	4
p.13	paragraph	6
p.14	paragraph	4
p.15	paragraph	3
p.15	paragraph	1 2
p.16	paragraph	1

Find each clue in turn and make notes in your rough book about the BFG. (You may prefer to use the original BFG book for your research).

Now, make up a BFG of your own - or a BBG if you like!

What does he look like? What clothes is he wearing?

What does he do?

Write all about him then draw a picture of him.

"The BFG can hear the tread of a ladybird's footsteps as she walks across a leaf. He can hear the whisperings of ants..."

Read this paragraph from Chapter 2, page 14.

Sit very quietly for few minutes and write down all the sounds you can hear.

If you had very sensitive hearing like the BFG what other sounds might you hear?

Read the first paragraph of Chapter 8.

To talk about

Danny describes the silence in the wood. Imagine that you are there in the wood with him, what sounds might you hear?

Perhaps you have read the BFG.

"In the moonlight, Sophie caught a glimpse of an enormous long pale wrinkly face with the most enormous ears... Sophie gave a yelp and pulled back from the window. She flew across the dormitory and jumped into her bed and hid under the blanket."

What happened next? Could you tell the story <u>briefly</u> to those people who don't know it?

Why do you think the BFG is such a popular story?

Make a list of other good books for children of your own age or younger.

What makes a good book/story do you think?

Make up an exciting story for young children based on some kind of giant.

Sequencing activity

To make a kite you need:-
>   6 thin sticks
>   material or polythene
>   a ball of string
>   glue or sticky tape

Cut two lengths of string off the main ball for tying the sticks.

Arrange 4 sticks in a star shape and tie with string.

Brace with 2 more sticks.

Cut the material to fit the star shape.

Put the material on the star shape and turn over the edges.

Stick down the edges with glue or sticky tape.

Cut out small pieces of material and tie these to a piece of string at intervals of half a metre to make a tail.

Fasten the tail to the kite.

Fasten the ball of string to the middle of the kite where the sticks cross.

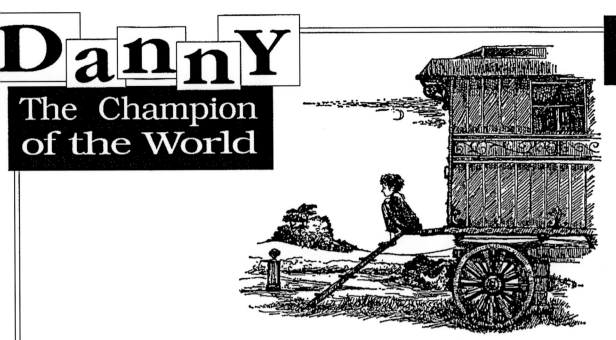

When you have read Chapter 4 answer these questions to make a summary of it:-

1. Why did Danny begin to feel a touch of panic?

2. Where had his father been?

3. Danny was shocked to find out where his dad had been. What excuses did his father give for his behaviour?

To talk about

Is a poacher the same as a thief do you think?

What would you think of a poacher if you were the rich man who owned the wood?

For drama

In a group of three, choose one person to be a poacher, one to be a gamekeeper and one to be a landowner. Work out what you think might happen when the poacher was caught with a brace of pheasants.

What is a <u>brace</u> of pheasants?

Danny
The Champion of the World

Write a summary of what happens in Chapter 4. Be sure to include the answers to these questions:-

1. Why did Danny begin to feel a touch of panic?

2. What was the explanation for his father's disappearance?

3. How did Danny's father try to justify poaching:-

        a) by his own dad, Danny's grandad
        b) by himself

For discussion

What do you think of people who poach? Would your opinion change, do you think,

        a) if you were the landowner?
        b) if you were poor and hungry?

What sorts of 'game' are commonly poached?

For drama

In a group of three choose one person to be a magistrate, one a solicitor defending the poacher, and one a solicitor prosecuting.

Act out a court-room scene where each solicitor states his case and the magistrate gives his ruling.

Introductory Discussion   (Teacher led)

Think back to when you first came to this school.
You wanted to know what the teachers were like.
How did you find out?

a. Brother/sister/friends talked about them.
b. Looked at teachers' appearance, their gestures
   and mannerisms.
c. What they sounded like - voice itself, the way
   they speak, things they say.
d. How they treated you and other pupils: whether they
   were strict, fair, kind, humourous.
   Can we trust this evidence?

Brief discussion about appearance/reality e.g. the boy
with a smart uniform and specs is always thought
to be brainy. People who look similar don't always behave
in the same way - we need more than one piece of
evidence before drawing conclusions about a person e.g.
that she is kind or bad-tempered.

N.B. Children will need to understand how to recognise
a paragraph and learn to count paragraphs by counting
the indentations down the left hand side of the page.
Count part-paragraphs at top of page as number 1.

Finding out about people. 1

We can judge people's character, that is we can find out what they are like, in several different ways:

1) other people tell us about them.
2) we watch them to see how they look and behave.
3) we hear what they sound like.

Find out about the teachers in Danny's school.
Turn to chapter 12 (pages 93 and 94) and read the paragraph about Miss Birdseye. Write the answers to the following questions to make a paragraph about this teacher.

1) What does the author tell us about Miss Birdseye?
2) What does Miss Birdseye do when the children are good?
   What does this action make you think of her?
3) What does her name "Miss Birdseye" make you think of her?

To talk about:

Do you think what you have written about Miss Birdseye is true? Did you have enough evidence to form a complete picture of her?
Is there any more evidence in the next paragraph which might help you to prove what you say?

Finding out about people. 2

Find out about Mr. Corrado. Read the paragraph about this teacher in chapter 12 (page 94 to 95).
Write your answers to the following questions to make one paragraph about Mr. Corrado.

1) What does Danny tell us about him?
2) What do his actions suggest about his character?

For discussion:

How true is Danny's opinion of his teacher likely to be? Do you think you have enough information to form a complete picture of him? What do you imagine he would do if someone in his class misbehaved?

Finding out about people. 3

Find out about Mr. Snoddy, (pages 95, 96, chapter 12). Write your answers to the following questions as a paragraph.

1) What did other people think of Mr. Snoddy according to Danny?
2) What did he look like? What does his appearance suggest about his character?
3) What particular habit did Mr. Snoddy have and what does it suggest about him?

For discussion:

On page 97 Danny's father talks about Mr. Snoddy. Does his opinion explain Mr. Snoddy's behaviour? Does this confirm your earlier opinion of him?

Finding out about people. 4

Find out about Captain Lancaster. Read about him
in chapter 12 (page 95.) Answer the following questions
to make one paragraph about Danny's teacher.

1) What two things does the author <u>tell us</u> about him?
2) What does Captain Lancaster look like?
   What does this make you think about him?
3) Why do you think he calls himself Captain instead
   of just plain Mister?
4) What does Captain Lancaster do?
   What do these habits make you think of him?

To talk about

When you have finished writing about Captain Lancaster,
read pages 98, 99, 100 and 101. What do think about
him now? Was what you wrote about him true? What else
have you found out? For instance what does the way
he talks tell us about him?
When you have talked about it in your group, put your
new ideas at the end of the earlier paragraph.

DannY

The Champion of the World

Captain Lancaster

A teacher called Captain Lancaster took the nine and ten year olds and this year that included me. Captain Lancaster, known sometimes as Lankers, was a _____ man. He had fiery carrot-c_____ hair and a little clipped carrotty _____ and a fiery temper. Carrotty coloured hairs were also sprouting out of his n_____ and his earholes. He had been a Captain in the army during the _____ against Hitler and that is why he still calls himself Captain Lancaster instead of just plain M_____ . My father said it was an idiotic thing to do. There were millions of people still alive, he said, who had _____ in that war, but most of them wanted to forget the whole beastly thing, especially those crummy military titles. Captain Lancaster was a v_____ man, and we were all terrified of him. He used to sit at his desk s_____ his carrotty moustache and watching us with pale watery blue _____ searching for trouble. And as he sat there, he would make queer snuffling _____ through his nose, like some dog s_____ round a rabbit hole.

Finding out about people. 5

Find out about Mr. Hazell. Read the beginning of chapter 6 and the beginning of chapter 20. Answer the following questions to make a paragraph about him.

1) What does Mr. Victor Hazell look like?
2) What does his appearance suggest about his character?
3) How did Mr. Hazell treat Danny and his father?
4) Why does Danny's father dislike him so much?
5) How do Danny and his father get their <u>revenge</u> in the end?

To talk about:

Read chapter 20 again. What would Mr. Hazell say to his shooting party guests when they got back?

Drama:

In pairs, choose one person to be Mr. Hazell and one to be a guest - perhaps the chief constable of the county - and act out this scene.

5g	Face	Hair	Clothes	Good points	Bad points	Other information
Danny						
Danny's father						
Mr. Hazell						
Doc Spencer						
Miss Birdseye						
Mr. Corrado						
Cpt. Lancaster						
Mr. Snoddy						

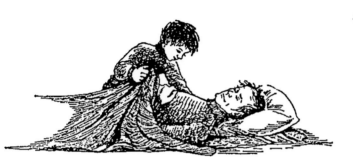

Quite a lot happens to Danny in his ninth year.
If he looked back and tried to write down all that
he had learned, what do you think he would write
under the following headings?

1. What I have learned about my father...

2. What I have learned about human nature...

3. What I have learned about poaching...

4. What I have learned about myself...

What's the Word?

Clues 2

Clues Down

1. Pheasants are crazy about r_____.
2. The man with the Rolls Royce and bad manners:
   Mr. H_____.
3. A kind teacher who likes gin.
4. This lady pushed the pram.
   Mrs. C_____.
5. Danny lived in this.
6. He looked after Danny's father when he broke his ankle.
7. The surname of the local policeman.

Clues Across

6. His name is in the title of the book.
8. This game bird is good to eat.
9. This teacher gave out aniseed balls.
10. A Captain with a carrotty moustache.
11. The car that Danny drove to Hazell's Wood.
    B_____ A_____.
12. He was in love with 9 across.

What's the Word?

Answers

Across:

8. pheasant
9. Miss Bird Seye
6. Danny
10. Lancaster
11. Baby Austin
12. Mr Corrado

Down:

1. raisins
2. Hazell
3. Mr Snodd
4. Clipstone
5. caravan
7. Stanways
6. Spencer

Clues across

1. Danny and his father sleep in these.
2. He's the villain of the story.
3. Captain Lancaster's hair is this colour.
4. She pushed the pram.
5. With 1 down, one of Danny's presents from his father.
6. This bird makes a good roast.
7. Raisins are this when you soak them in water.
8. Danny's father broke this when he fell.
9. With 12 across, Danny's best friend.
10. The author of "Danny".
11. They liked to be tickled.
12. See 9 across.
13. Danny needed one of these to light his way in the wood.
14. Mr. Snoddy's favourite tipple.
15. These were hidden inside Mrs. Spencer's meat pie.
16. The "getaway" driver.
17. Danny's father fell into it.
18. Mr. Hazell's registration plate.
19. What all parents should be.

Clues down

1. With 5 across, one of Danny's presents from his father.
2. Sergeant Samway's christian name.
3. This game doesn't fly.
4. The big giant was this.
5. Danny's father's name.
6. The fuel used in the caravan.
7. How many hundreds of raisins did they use?
8. This is the time for poachers to go out to work.
9. The name of Danny's go-kart.
10. Mr. Hazell's car.
11. Our hero.
12. Danny's pet name for the Captain.
14. One of Mr. Hazell's guests might use this to bag a pheasant.
15. Spencer's title.
16. Danny's father made these for him.
17. Captian Lancaster used this on Danny.
18. This was needed to get Danny's father out of the pit.
19. He sat on the catch of pheasants.
20. You need this to make "The Sticky Hat".

Answers

Design a "Danny" crossword

Design a crossword using clues from "Danny the Champion of the World". The grid below will help you set it out. Here are some interesting words to get you started.

Horace
o
r
s
e
h
a
i
r

B
i
g
f
r
i
e
d
l
y

filling station

poacher's bottom

r
o
s
t
e
r

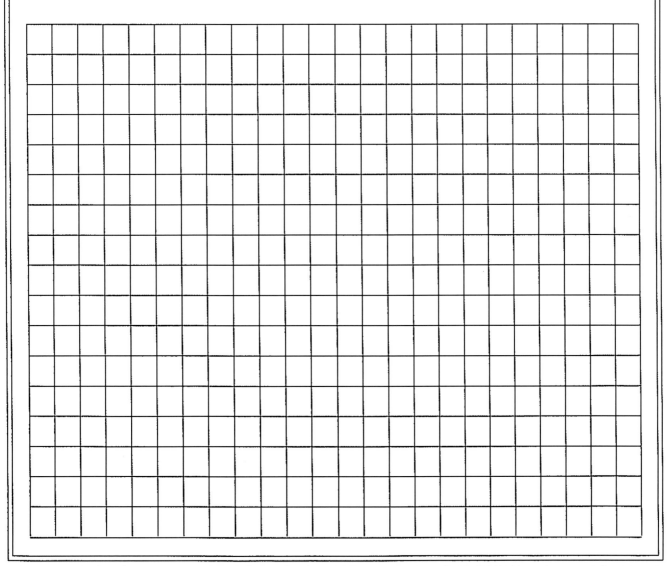

Spelling sheets: Look, Cover, Write, Check.

1. Look

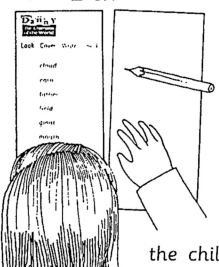

You may like to use the spelling sheets with pupils as a way of practising spelling skills. The words are some of those which they will see repeatedly during the reading of the book, and perhaps use in their writing, so spellings are being learned in context.

Choose a list appropriate to the child: if ten words are too many to learn in one go, give him a list of five.

2. Cover and Write

Lists "a" tend to include the more common, everyday words which the children will be using more regularly: lists "b" are made up of slightly more difficult or unusual words: lists "c" contain the more flamboyant and awkward-to-spell words which should challenge even the "good" spellers!

3. Check

Always encourage pupils to use the LOOK COVER WRITE CHECK method to learn spelling and check themselves: they can work with "spelling partners" to check each other.

Danny The Champion of the World

Look - Cover - Write - Check

cloud	
earn	
father	
field	
giant	
mouth	
night	
through	
tight	
world	

1a

Danny The Champion of the World

Look - Cover - Write - Check

build	
built	
caravan	
drawer	
enough	
except	
marvellous	
serious	
station	
wonderful	

1b

Danny The Champion of the World

Look - Cover - Write - Check

bough	
ceiling	
enormous	
especially	
gypsy	
gypsies	
mysterious	
paraffin	
tremendous	
whisper	

1c

Danny
The Champion of the World

Look - Cover - Write - Check

edge

engine

enough

fire

knew

repair

round

school

shirt

village

2a

Danny
The Champion of the World

Look - Cover - Write - Check

attach

believe

compliment

different

exactly

famous

imagine

impatient

pieces

promise

2b

Danny
The Champion of the World

Look - Cover - Write - Check

absolute

actually

certainly

completely

engineer

extremely

magnificent

mechanic

pheasant

scissors

2c

Danny — The Champion of the World

Look - Cover - Write - Check

- behind
- caught
- cloud
- crumb
- dirty
- either
- known
- quickly
- used
- watching

3a

Danny — The Champion of the World

Look - Cover - Write - Check

- believe
- discover
- doubt
- length
- ordinary
- pause
- poaching
- sausage
- shoulders
- silence

3b

Danny — The Champion of the World

Look - Cover - Write - Check

- beautiful
- beauty
- brilliance
- celebration
- excitement
- discovery
- ghosts
- listening
- pleasure
- pyjamas

3c

Danny The Champion of the World

Look - Cover - Write - Check

always

answer

brake

brighter

earth

easy

knew

minute

quiet

walking

4a

Danny The Champion of the World

Look - Cover - Write - Check

describe

echoed

exact

listened

quarter

searching

sweater

travel

travelling

twilight

4b

Danny The Champion of the World

Look - Cover - Write - Check

accelerator

anaesthetic

breakfast

chassis

collapsed

frightful

ignition

mechanical

motionless

wounded

4c

Danny The Champion of the World

Look - Cover - Write - Check

autumn

bottle

cheat

country

heard

nearly

point

prove

uniform

which

5a

Danny The Champion of the World

Look - Cover - Write - Check

ambulance

disappear

district

divide

impossible

instead

paused

thread

tomorrow

wedge

5b

Danny The Champion of the World

Look - Cover - Write - Check

ancient

capsule

celebrates

fascinating

idiotic

occasion

patient

spectacles

tongue

treasure

5c

Danny
The Champion of the World

Look - Cover - Write - Check

behind

crawl

flavour

hungry

knife

minute

pocket

proud

tense

tonight

6a

Danny
The Champion of the World

Look - Cover - Write - Check

dangerous

distance

favourite

guard

instead

miracle

ploughed

saucepan

scarce

sweater

6b

Danny
The Champion of the World

Look - Cover - Write - Check

discoloured

extraordinary

incredible

motionless

moustache

peculiar

respectable

stomach

succulent

wounded

6c

Reading the Play:
(Teacher's Notes)

● The number of lines for each character is indicated in brackets: Sgt. Samway's is by far the longest part and will require a reader who can cope with the dropped h's and use good expression to make full use of the humour.

● Allow readers preparation time before reading aloud, help them out with any difficult words.

● Readers can use a high-lighter pen to mark their own parts and help them to come in 'on cue'.

● Remind readers that the stage directions, in shaded print, are not to be read out - unless you choose a 'narrator' to do this specifically.

Some possible extension activities:

● Sound effects

● Record onto audio tape

● Video

● Extract the speech from another part of the book, to make a different scene.

● Write another play e.g.   What happened the next day
                              Mrs Clipstone returns home
                              Sgt Samways back at the station
                              Mr Hazell goes to see his M.P.

- - - - - - - - - - CUT - - - - - - - - - -

Mr Hazell's
come - uppance

A Play based on Danny
the Champion of the World

Mr Hazell's Come - uppance

> Mrs Clipstone is delivering the pheasants in the specially adapted pram when gradually the effects of the sleeping pills begin to wear off and one-by-one the birds escape...

Doc Spencer : Great Scott! I know what's happened! It's the sleeping pills! They're wearing off!

> Mrs. Clipstone hurtles into the filling station with birds flying out in all directions.

Mrs Clipstone : What on earth is happening?

> Baby is screaming as she lifts him from the pram. More birds escape.

Doc Spencer : A sleeping pill doesn't last forever. It always wears off by the next morning.

Mrs Clipstone : They nearly pecked him to pieces!

Dad : Take him into the caravan, Mrs. Clipstone. All these birds are making him nervous. Danny - push that pram into the workshop, quick!

CUT

Mr Hazell's come - uppance

Cast: Danny (9)

Dad (41)

Mrs Clipstone (45)

Mr Hazell (41)

Sgt Samways (70)

Doc Spencer (41)

Sgt Samways : Well, well, well. What, may I ask, is appenin around ere?

Mr Hazell : I'll tell you what's happening round here. These are MY pheasants, and this rogue has enticed them out of my woods on to his filthy little filling station.

Sgt. Samways: Hen-ticed? Hen-ticed them did you say?

Mr Hazell : Of course he enticed them!

Sgt Samways : Well now. This is a very hinterestin haccusation, very hinterestin indeed, because I ain't never eard of nobody hen-ticin a pheasant across six miles of fields and open countryside. Ow do think this hen-ticin' was performed, Mr. Azell, if I may ask?

Mr Hazell : Don't ask me HOW he did it. I don't know! But he's done it alright! The proof is all around you! All my finest birds are sitting here in this dirty little filling station when they ought to be up in my own wood getting ready for the shoot!

---- CUT ----

Danny pushes pram into workshop, a line of traffic begins to form and people get out of their cars to see what is happening. Mr Hazell pulls up in his Rolls Royce:

Danny : Watch out Dad. Look who's here.

Mr Hazell : (Shouting angrily) What on earth do you think you're doing, you thieving rogue? How dare you! How dare you steal my pheasants... I'll have your filthy hide for this, just you see if I don't. I'll see you locked away where you belong...

Dad : But they're not your pheasants, they're mine.

Mr Hazell : Don't lie to me man! They're mine. I'm the only person round here who has pheasants!

Dad : They are on my land. They flew onto my land and so long as they stay on my land they belong to me. Don't you know the rules, you bloated old blue-faced baboon?

Mr Hazell is about to explode. He looks at the dopey birds.

Mr Hazell : What's the matter with em? What have you done to em?

4

Sgt Samways : Am I correct, am I habsolutely haccurate in thinkin that today is the day of your great shootin party, Mr. Azell?

Mr Hazell : That's the whole point! If I don't get these birds back on my land quick sharp, some very important people are going to be extremely angry - including your own boss, Sergeant, The Chief Constable of the County! So you had better do something fast, unless you want to lose those sergeant's stripes of yours.

Sgt Samways : Now just one minute. Just one minute please. Am I to understand that you are haccusin this gentleman ere of committin this act?

Mr Hazell : Of course I am. I KNOW he did it!

Sgt Samways : And do you ave any evidence to support this haccusation?

Mr Hazell : The evidence is all around you! Are you blind or something?

Dad (quietly) : Surely you know how these pheasants came to be here?

Mr Hazell : Surely I do NOT know.

- - - - - - - - - - - - CUT - - - - - - - - - - - -

5

Dad : Then I shall tell you, because it's quite simple really. They all knew they were going to be shot today if they stayed in your wood, so they flew in here to wait until the shooting was over.

Mr Hazell : Rubbish!

Dad : It's not rubbish at all. They are extremely intelligent birds, pheasants. Isn't that so doctor?

Doc Spencer : They have tremendous brain power. They know exactly what's going on.

Dad : It would undoubtedly be a great honour to be shot by the Chief Constable of the County, and an even greater one to be eaten afterwards by Lord Thistlethwaite, but I don't think a pheasant would see it that way.

Mr Hazell : You are scoundrels, both of you! You are rapscallions of the worst kind!

Sgt Samways : Now then, now then. Hinsults ain't goin to get us nowhere. They only haggravate things. Therefore, gentlemen, I ave a

suggestion to put before you. I suggest that we - all of us - make a big heffort to drive these birds back over the road on to Mr. Azell's land. ow does that strike you Mr. Azell?

Mr Hazell : It'll be a step in the right direction. Get on with it then.

Sgt Samways : Ow about you Willum? Are you agreeable to this haction?

Dad : I think it's a splendid idea. I'll be glad to help, so will Danny.

> Dad and Sgt. Samways exchange 'knowing looks'.

Sgt Samways : Come on my lads! Let's push these lazy birds over the road.

> (Strides around waving his arms and shouting) Shoo, shoo! Off you go. Get out of here.

> The others join in and soon the pheasants are all over Mr. Hazell's Rolls Royce.

Mr Hazell : Get them off! Get them away!

Sgt Samways : Don't worry Mr. Azell, sir . We'll fix em for you. Come on boys! Heasy does it! Shoo em right over the road!

Mr Hazell : Not on my car, you idiot! Send them the other way!

Sgt Samways : We will sir, we will!

Mr Hazell : Get those birds off my car! Can't you see they're ruining the paintwork, you madman!

Sgt Samways : Paintwork? What paintwork? We've done our very best to hencourage these birds over the road but they're too hignorant to understand.

Mr Hazell : My car man! Get them away from my car!

Sgt Samways : Ah. Your car . Yes, I see what you mean sir. Beastly, dirty birds, pheasants are. But why don't you just op in quick and drive er away fast? They'll ave to get off then, won't they?

> Mr Hazell gets into his car amid much flapping and squawking.

Dad : Well, it was really Danny's idea. He invented a new method called 'The Sleeping beauty', go on, Danny, you tell him.

Danny : I got the idea when Doc Spencer gave Dad some sleeping tablets after he hurt his ankle. I thought they might put pheasants to sleep just as they do with people.

Sgt Samways : Well I never! But how did you get them birds to swallow the pills?

Danny : Oh that was easy - we emptied the powder into nice, fat, juicy raisins! The pheasants loved them!

Sgt Samways : Well I'll be blowed! You could knock me down with a feather! Stone the crows! Well I'll be jiggered! I never would have thought a little nipper like you could come up with a fantastical brainwave like that. Young man, I congratulate you!

Doc Spencer : He'll go a long way, young Danny will, you see if he doesn't. He'll be a great inventor one day.

[Mrs Clipstone emerges from the caravan.]

----------------------------- CUT -----------------------------

Sgt Samways : Drive on Mr Azell, sir. Urry up, urry up urry up! get goin quick! There's no time to lose! Hignore them pheasants Mr Azell.

[Mr Hazell starts up his engine and drives away. Sergeant Samways tries to disperse the queue of traffic which has built up.]

Sgt Samways : Come along now! Get movin. Get goin! We can't have this, you're blockin the ighway!

[Engines start up and the traffic moves along.]

Sgt Samways : Well, Willum. Them pheasants was the most hastonishin sight I ever seed in my hentire life!

Doc Spencer : It was lovely. Just lovely. Didn't you enjoy it Danny?

Danny : Marvellous. It really was marvellous.

Dad : Pity we lost them. It very near broke my heart when they all started flying out of the pram. I knew we'd lost them then.

Sgt Samways : But how in eaven's name did you ever catch em in the first place? Ow did you do it Willum? Come on man, let me in on the secret.

10

Mrs Clipstone : Well thank goodness that's over at last. Never in my life have I seen such a shambles as that. What a gathering we have here of rogues and varmints! Good morning Enoch.

Sgt Samways : Good morning to you, Mrs Clipstone.

Dad ; How's the baby?

Mrs Clipstone : The baby is better, thankyou William. though I doubt he'll ever be the quite same again.

Doc Spencer : Of course he will. Babies are tough.

Mrs Clipstone : I don't care how tough they are! How would YOU like it if you were being taken for a nice quiet walk in your pram on a fine autumn morning... and you were sitting on a lovely soft mattress... and suddenly the mattress comes alive and starts bouncing you up and down like a stormy sea... and the next thing you know, there's about a hundred sharp, curvy beaks poking up from underneath the mattress and pecking you to pieces!

CUT

Doc Spencer is smiling, and trying not to laugh.

Mrs Clipstone : You think it's funny! Well, just you wait, Doctor Spencer and one night I'll put a few snakes or crocodiles or something under YOUR mattress and see how you like it!

Sgt Samways has collected his bicycle from beside the pumps.

Sgt Samways : Well, ladies and gents, I must be off and see who else is getting into mischief round ere.

Dad : I am truly sorry you were troubled Enoch. And thanks very much indeed for the help.

Sgt Samways : I wouldn't ave missed this for all the tea in China. But it did sadden me most terrible, Willum, to see all those lovely birds go slippin through our fingers like that. Because to my mind, there don't hexist a more luscious dish than roasted pheasant anywhere on this earth.

Mrs Clipstone : It's going to sadden the vicar a lot more than it saddens you! That's all he's been talking about ever

11

Doc Spencer : since he got home this morning - the lovely roast pheasant he's going to have for his dinner tonight!

Doc Spencer : He'll get over it.

Mrs Clipstone : He will NOT get over it and it's a rotten shame, because all I've got to give him now are some awful fillets of cod, and he never did like cod anyway.

Dad : But surely you didn't load all of those pheasants into the pram did you? You were meant to keep at least a dozen for you and the vicar!

Mrs Clipstone : (Wailing) Oh I know that. But I was so tickled at the thought of strolling calmly through the village with Christopher sitting on a hundred and twenty birds, I simply forgot to keep back any for ourselves. And now, alas, they're all gone! And so is the vicar's supper!

Doc Spencer : You come with me Grace (Taking her by the arm) I've got something to show you.

He leads her into the workshop.

12

--- CUT ---

Mrs Clipstone : (Calling from inside the workshop) Good grief! Come and look at this. William, Enoch, Danny! Come and look!

Inside the workshop. Six magnificent pheasants are lying among the spanners and wrenches.

Doc Spencer : There you are ladies and gentlemen. How's that? Two for you Grace, to keep the vicar in a good mood. Two for Enoch for all the fine work he did this morning. And two for William and Danny, who deserves them most of all.

Dad : What about you Doctor? That doesn't leave any for you.

Doc Spencer : My wife has enough to do without plucking pheasants all day long. And anyway, who got them out of the wood in the first place? You and Danny.

Dad : But how on earth did YOU get them? When did you nab them?

Doc Spencer : I didn't nab them, I had a hunch.

Dad : What sort of a hunch?

Doc Spencer : It seemed fairly obvious that SOME of those pheasants must have gobbled up more than one

13

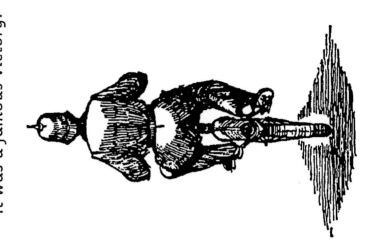

of the law cycling through the village with a brace of pheasants slung over the handle bars.

Sgt Samways : I am very much hobliged to you doctor. I really am.

Sgt Samways cycles away. Doc Spencer, Mrs Clipstone and the baby, get into the car. Danny and his father load the birds into the boot. Doc Spencer leans out of the window as he drives away....

Doc Spencer : Don't be sad William. It was a famous victory!

15

-------------------- CUT --------------------

raisin each. Some, if they were quick enough might have swallowed half a dozen each, or even more. In which case they would have received a very heavy overdose of sleeping pills and wouldn't EVER wake up.

Everybody : Ah-ha. Of course. Of course.

Doc Spencer : So while you were all so busy driving the birds on to old Hazell's Rolls Royce, I sneaked in here and had a look under the sheet in the pram. And there they were!

Sgt Samways : Hamazin. Habsolutely hamazin!

Doc Spencer : Those were the greedy ones. It never pays to eat more than your fair share.

Dad : Marvellous. Well done sir!

Mrs Clipstone : Oh, you lovely man. (gives him a big kiss on the cheek)

Doc Spencer : Now come along. I'll drive you home. You can leave this crazy perambulator where it is. And Enoch, we'll take your birds with us and drop off at your house on the way. We can't have the arm

14